BIG MAGIC NUMBER PUZZLES

36 Exciting Puzzles to Promote Math Learning and Logical-Thinking Skills

by Allyne Brumbaugh

SCHOLASTIC
PROFESSIONAL BOOKS

New York • Toronto • London • Auckland • Sydney

Designed by Ellen Matlach Hassell for
Boultinghouse and Boultinghouse, Inc.

Cover design by Vincent Ceci

Illustration by Rick Brown

ISBN 0-590-49275-6

12 11 10 9 8 7 6 5 4   6 7 8/9

Printed in the U.S.A.

To my second graders at

Greenacres Elementary School

Scarsdale, New York,

who worked so hard on these puzzles,

and

To Jim

TABLE OF CONTENTS

Note to Teachers

As an elementary school teacher I'm always on the lookout for math puzzles, games, and tricks that will make math more fun for my students. At the same time, I want to reinforce concepts and give them opportunities to acquire some new mathematical insights.

The Magic Number puzzles on the following pages are so popular in my second grade classroom that they have become an integral part of my enrichment math program. Colleagues teaching in the upper grades have had equal success using the puzzles (although they *still* don't quite believe that second graders can do them). Many of the puzzles in this volume are quite well known. Others, I've adapted or made up myself to meet my students' demands for more puzzles.

What do children learn? For starters, my children learn that problems may have more than one solution and that there are different ways to find solutions. They learn to work cooperatively and to be persistent. They develop and strengthen skills such as estimation and logical reasoning. They devise strategies and learn the strategies of their classmates. They learn that math is fun! But the learning doesn't stop there. One of the most valuable learning experiences to come out of my Magic Number puzzle program is cooperative learning. As you'll see, students working on Magic Number puzzles quickly begin forming cooperative groups. These groups motivate children to share strategies, brainstorm solutions, and encourage each other when they get stuck. Children working in groups develop a sense of comraderie and cooperation that is a big plus to any learning environment. (See pages 22, 24, 28, 30, 62, and 66 for hints for working with groups in your classroom.)

Classroom management is an added bonus. Once the puzzles take hold I never hear "What should I do now?" when an assignment is finished. These number puzzles are the first thing my kids reach for.

Happy Solving!

What Is a Magic Number Puzzle?

Generally, this term refers to a type of puzzle in which specified numbers are arranged in a pattern such that each row, column, and diagonal adds up to the same sum.

The most well-known of these puzzles is the Magic Square (see pages 10–11).

How to Use This Book

1. It's best to start out by photocopying class sets of the first few puzzles and placing them in folders. As children finish one puzzle they can take the next one on their own. Continue to photocopy class sets of remaining puzzles as you need them.

2. I always give children numbered disks to use. They can experiment with the placement of each number, move the numbers around, start over again—all without having to keep writing and erasing (my kids don't seem to like to mess up their papers). When they are satisfied with their solutions they can write the numbers in the correct spaces.

    Although I usually use 1-inch plastic counters, you'll find some reproducible disks on page 78, which also work nicely. To make the disks ready to use, simply distribute photocopied sheets to students, asking each to cut out his or her own disks. If you choose to purchase 1-inch plastic counters, you can either write the numbers directly on them with magic marker, or cover them with ³/₄-inch self-sticking paper circles and write on the circles. (If you cover both sides with the paper circles children can write their initials on the back of each disk.) You can even cover pennies with the stick-on circles and use them in place of the plastic counters. Give each child the numbers 1 through 9 to start with. (They will need higher numbers later.) Store disks in individual plastic zip-lock bags, keeping a few extra sets to replace misplaced disks.

3. I find it best to have children do the puzzles in the order they are printed in the book. As students progress through the puzzles, they'll gain knowledge and experience that will assist them in solving more difficult puzzles.

    Each puzzle is accompanied by notes that detail techniques for solving the puzzles or outline strategies for class management. The notes also include solutions to each puzzle.

4. Although children work at their own pace, independently or in small groups, I always start them off together on the simplest puzzle: The Magic I.

Notes on the Magic I

Most children will achieve quick success with this puzzle. The numbers (1 through 7) and the sum of each row (12) are simple to work with. To make it even easier the center number (4) is provided as a hint.

After explaining how magic puzzles work and showing students the first few, give each child a copy of the Magic I puzzle and a set of numbers. Most children can't wait to start, although others are not in such a big hurry. (This *is* after all, still math.)

The center number is the key to this puzzle. Since it must work in three rows (the two diagonals and the vertical) the only number that will work is 4.

Most children will use a guess-and-check method, trying various combinations adding up to 12 until they come up with a solution. For younger or less able math students you may want to suggest using 12 objects (Unifix cubes work really well), breaking the manipulatives up into three groups to find combinations of 12 that use three addends.

Here is one solution:

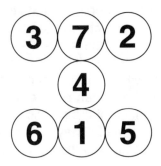

MAGIC I

4

Use the numbers 1–7.

Each row (horizontal, vertical, and diagonal) must add up to 12.

Notes on the Magic Square

The Magic Square is one of the most well known of the Magic Number puzzles. Your students may even have encountered this one before in mathematical game and puzzle books.

Again, the center number is provided as a hint. This time the numbers 1 through 9 are used and the magic sum is 15.

Most children will find this puzzle a bit more challenging but not difficult enough to be frustrating.

One solution is:

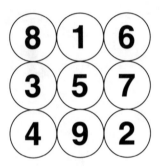

MAGIC SQUARE

5

Use the numbers 1–9.

Each row (horizontal, vertical, and diagonal) must add up to 15.

Notes on the Magic C

The Magic C is the first puzzle in which no hint is given. Children are inclined to work one row at a time and then start all over if the last row doesn't add up to 15. Some children will attempt to fix the incorrect row.

(3)(4)(8) = 15
(6)
(1)
(5)(2)(7) = 14
=
15

(3)(4)(7) = 14
(6)
(1)
(5)(2)(8) = 15
=
15

Recognizing that the bottom horizontal row needs one more, students may exchange the 7 in this row with the 8 in the top row. This does, indeed, fix the bottom row but now the top row is one short.

Other children will recognize that there are two key points in this puzzle—the points where the horizontal rows intersect with the vertical row. A number placed at one of these intersecting points can be exchanged with a nonintersecting number in the vertical row without harming a correct line.

In the first illustration, for example, if the 5 and the 6 are exchanged, the vertical row remains the same, while the bottom horizontal row now adds up to 15.

One correct solution for a sum of 15 is:

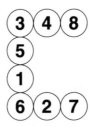

There are also solutions for sums of 13 and 16:

(2)(3)(8)
(6)
(4)
(1)(5)(7)

Sum = 13

(4)(7)(5)
(1)
(3)
(8)(6)(2)

Sum = 16

MAGIC C

Use the numbers 1–8.

Each row must equal 15.

Notes on the Magic T

With the Magic T, the question is whether to teach the technique as described on page 12 or to allow the children to discover it for themselves. I generally try to allow children to work it out for themselves—and most do. I intervene when children seem particularly frustrated. Once the concept is explained, some children grasp it completely. Others use the information for the particular puzzle they're working on but are unable to apply the technique to the next one—they're just not ready. I leave it to you to judge the needs of your students.

One solution to this puzzle is:

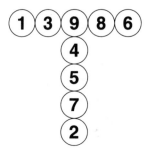

There are also solutions for the sums of 23, 24, 25, and 26. Each has a different number at the intersection point:

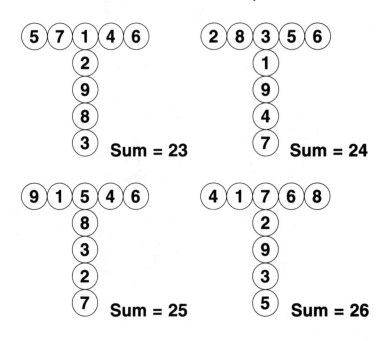

MAGIC T

Use the numbers 1–9.

Each row must equal 27.

Notes on the Magic Mini-Triangles

This puzzle is a bit different. Rather than trying to make each row add up to a specific sum, the object is to make the shapes (four triangles and the center diamond) add up to 12.

The easiest way to go about solving this one is to start with the diamond. Given the numbers 1 through 8, there are only two combinations of four numbers that equal 12. They are: 1, 2, 4, 5 and 1, 2, 3, 6.

Start with the 1, 2, 4, 5 combination in the diamond. Children will easily see that the 1 and 2 cannot be placed adjacent to each other because the third number in that triangle would have to be a 9, which is not an option. Putting the 1 and 2 opposite each other and the 4 and 5 opposite each other in the diamond would require another 5 and two 6's to make the triangles equal 12. Clearly, the 1, 2, 4, 5 is an impossible combination.

Using the 1, 2, 3, 6 for the diamond yields this solution:

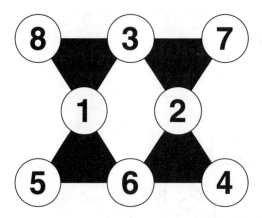

Some children, however, start with the triangles. As Stephanie and Jamie told me, "We knew we should put the high numbers on the outside corners of the triangle because if we put them on the inside corners it would make the diamond too high."

MAGIC MINI-TRIANGLES

Use the numbers 1–8.

Each of the four shaded triangles and the center diamond must equal 12.

Notes on the Magic Y

This is the first puzzle that uses a number beyond 9. Children will need a 10 disk to solve the puzzle.

The Magic Y is not an easy puzzle. The center number is the key one. Once it is selected, the other three numbers in each row must be equal.

Children generally keep trying different numbers in the center until they find one that works (7).

A correct solution is:

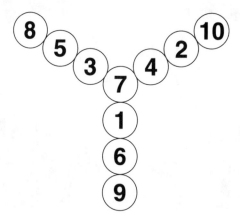

Other sums that work for this puzzle are 19 and 21.

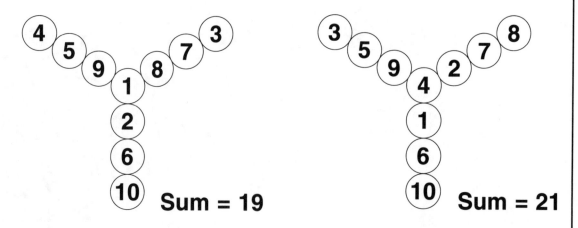

MAGIC Y

Use the numbers 1–10 so
that each row equals 23.

Notes on the Magic Bow

By this time great excitement has generally built up in my classroom over these puzzles. Most kids rush into the room the moment the bell rings and get out their number disks and puzzles. Even children who are not usually math enthusiasts are drawn to the puzzles.

The Magic Bow introduces the number 11. Again, the center number is key. Although there is no definite way to know what the center number should be, children who start out using a low center number quickly discover that they don't have enough high numbers to make all the rows add up to 20.

Using 7 or 9 in the center will yield a correct solution:

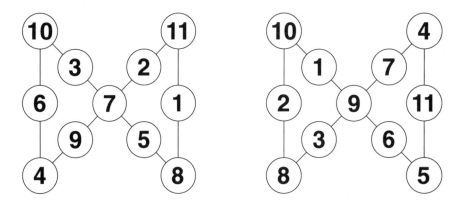

As you can see, the sum of the two remaining numbers in each row radiating from the center is equal (13 when 7 is in the center or 11 when 9 is in the center). If opposite rows are paired up properly, the two remaining numbers will fit correctly into the vertical rows.

MAGIC BOW

Use the numbers 1–11 so that each of the six rows of three circles equals 20.

21

Notes on the Magic E

There's a twist to this puzzle. Not only each of the four rows must add up to 19, but the total of the four "corners" must equal 19, too.

A solution for the sum of 19 is:

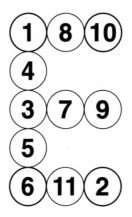

There are also solutions for the sums of 18 and 20:

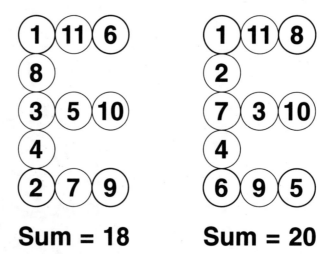

At this point groups have started to form naturally in my room as children who are working on the same puzzles begin to work together.

Name _____   Date _____

MAGIC E

Use the numbers 1–11 to make each row equal 19.

The total of the four "corners" must be 19, too.

23

Notes on the Magic 26

Each year, at Open House, I explain to parents the rationale for using these puzzles. I'm occasionally asked about the advisability of having children work in groups. The question really is: "If Emily comes up with the answer and gives it to the rest of the group, then have Josh and Ben really solved the puzzle?"

My answer is: "Yes. If Emily, Josh, and Ben have worked on the puzzle as a team, then it doesn't really matter which child actually 'solved' the puzzle. The process is most important." In any event, one of the other children generally comes up with the solution to the next puzzle.

However, it is a situation you will have to monitor. One year, Peter (a particularly adept math student) was working with Michael and Russell (also strong math students, but not as quick). Peter was getting all the answers to the easier number puzzles before the other two boys had much of a chance to try. Peter happily shared his solutions but Mike and Russ felt they weren't having any "fun." I asked Peter to go ahead on his own, which he did. When the puzzles got harder, he decided to wait for his friends to catch up, which they did. From then on, this group was able to work cooperatively on equal footing.

This puzzle uses numbers up to 12. Children are always amazed by the number of ways this puzzle can add up to 26.

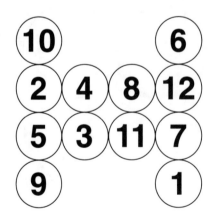

Name _____

Date _____

MAGIC 26

Use the numbers 1–12.

Each row, column, and diagonal must equal 26. The total of the four corners and the total of the four center numbers must equal 26, too.

Notes on the Magic Diamond

This is the first in a series of puzzles in which the magic sum is not given. After the initial shock ("What do you mean you're not going to tell us the sum?") has worn off, children who are up to this puzzle get right to it.

There is a mathematical way to find the range of possible sums:

Step 1—Since each of the numbers 1-12 are used at least once in this puzzle, add those numbers together to get a total of 78.

Step 2—Four numbers (those in the vertices) will be used twice. Try the lowest numbers first, adding 1, 2, 3, and 4 (10) to 78 for a new total of 88. Dividing 88 by 4 (the number of rows) will yield the lowest possible sum—in this case, 22. Therefore 22 (with vertices equaling 10) is the lowest *possible* sum—it may not be a sum that works but it is the lowest one possible. (If the total is not evenly divisible by the number of rows, then the next try would be vertices equaling 11, 12, 13, and so on.)

Step 3—To find the high end of the range use the highest numbers for the vertices. In this case:

$78 + 9 + 10 + 11 + 12 = 120 \div 4 = 30$

Therefore, 30 (with vertices equaling 42) is the highest possible sum. As it turns out, this puzzle can be solved for sums 22 through 30.

Clearly, this is not a useful technique for younger children (the children I teach are not able to use this method and many are still able to solve nearly every puzzle in this book using trial and error, estimation, and prior knowledge) but it is one that may be discovered by or taught to older children.

Solutions for sums 22, 25, and 30 are:

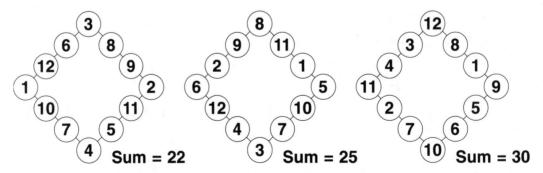

As noted above, there are also solutions for sums of 23, 24, 26, 27, 28, and 29.

MAGIC DIAMOND

Use the numbers 1–12.

Each row must equal the same sum.

Notes on the Magic Pentagon

The value of working in a group soon becomes apparent as students attack The Magic Pentagon:

"I'll try 16."

"You try 20."

"Thirty is too high."

The key numbers in the pentagon are the five vertices. Switching a center number with a vertex number will leave one row the same while making the other higher or lower.

In addition, the same technique used to solve the Magic Diamond will work with this puzzle.

Add: 1–10 = 55 + 1 + 2 + 3 + 4 + 5 = 70 ÷ 5 = 14 (lowest possible sum)
{lowest vertices}

Add: 1–10 = 55 + 6 + 7 + 8 + 9 + 10 = 95 ÷ 5 = 19 (highest possible sum)
{highest vertices}

There are four sums that yield solutions (14, 16, 17, and 19). Here are some arrangements that work:

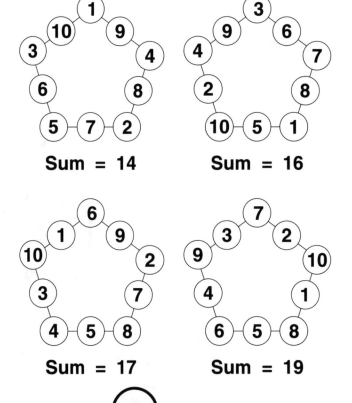

Sum = 14   Sum = 16

Sum = 17   Sum = 19

MAGIC PENTAGON

Use the numbers 1–10 so that
all sides of the pentagon equal
the same sum.

Notes on the Magic Hexagon

The Magic Hexagon is essentially the same as the Magic Pentagon and the Magic Diamond. The same strategies will work for all.

The lowest possible sum is 17. The highest is 22. Solutions for these sums, as well as for the sum of 20, are given below.

The first year I used Magic Number puzzles I thought that these "sumless" puzzles would mark a cutoff point. Children with less math ability would surely be frustrated and lose interest. And then a curious thing happened. The very children whom I predicted would never get the answers—did!

Johan was one of those students. When I asked him how he had arrived at the magic sum for this puzzle, he said "Oh, last week I was sitting next to Lisa and Nina when they got the Hexagon and I remembered it was 20."

The magic sums figured out by the first few groups gradually filter down to the very children who need a hint to make solving the puzzle possible. And neither the givers nor the receivers of these hints seem to have any problem with this strategy. I was and am delighted. Each child achieves success at his or her own level.

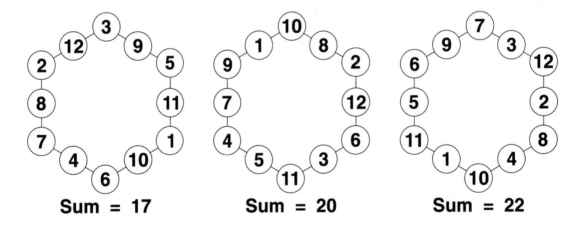

Sum = 17   Sum = 20   Sum = 22

MAGIC HEXAGON

Use the numbers 1–12.

Each side of the hexagon must have the same sum.

Notes on the Magic H

A few years ago I had a group of kids who, by the middle of the year, had finished every puzzle available. I decided to make one up for them. The result was the Magic H—the first magic number puzzle I constructed myself.

The construction took several hours. First I had to decide on a shape. Then I had to keep manipulating the numbers to come up with a workable sum. (At that time I hadn't yet figured out the technique for finding the highest and lowest possible sums.) Eventually, by trial and error, I worked it out so that each of the three rows and the total of the four corners equaled 35.

I took the puzzle to school the next day, confident that it would keep the kids going for several days. They took it to lunch and solved it in twenty minutes!

To find the range:

Add: 1–13 = 91 + 1 + 2 = 94 ÷ 3 = 31.333333 . . .
        {2 lowest numbers}

In this case using the two lowest numbers (1 and 2) as the vertices doesn't work because it doesn't yield a whole number.

The lowest possible sum turns out to be 32 (with vertices of 2 and 3). The highest is 38 (with vertices of 11 and 12).

Solutions for these, as well as 33, 34, 35, 36, and 37, are:

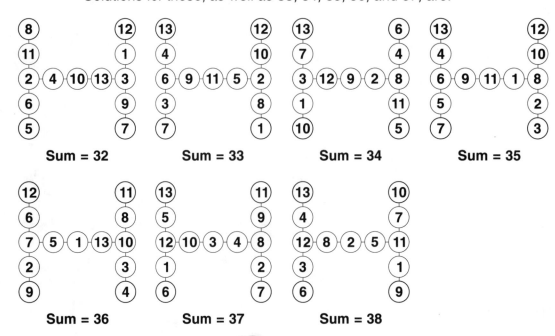

Name _____   Date _____

MAGIC H

Use the numbers 1–13.

- Each of the three rows and the total of the four corners must equal the same sum.

33

Notes on the Little Magic Wheel

This is the first of three puzzles that uses a central number several times and the other numbers once each.

Most children generally try to solve the Wheel puzzles by arbitrarily picking a number for the center and then trying different combinations, hoping for equal sums, in each row.

Some children take shortcuts by trying to find four sets of equal pairs to go with the center number.

More sophisticated math students will use a logical method to find the equal pairs. For example:

Choosing 4 for the center number, the remaining numbers are: 1, 2, 3, 5, 6, 7, 8, 9. Pairing the 1 and 9, 2 and 8, 3 and 7 yields an equal sum in each row (10). But the 5/6 combination doesn't work. Children can see that if they use the 5 as the center instead of the 4 they can then pair the 4 and 6. When these pairs are arranged around the central 5, the sum of each row will be 15.

The same strategy will work with 1 or 9 in the center spot.

Solutions are:

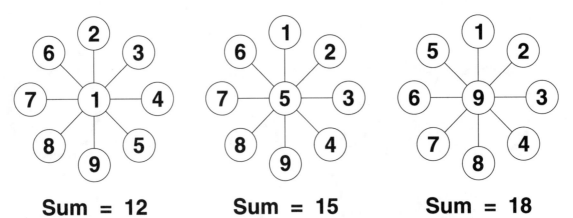

Sum = 12   **Sum = 15**   **Sum = 18**

LITTLE MAGIC WHEEL

Use the numbers 1–9 so that each of the four rows has the same sum.

Notes on the
Big Magic Wheel

A more sophisticated technique can be used to find the center number of a magic wheel.

Add the numbers used in the puzzle. Subtract the number you want to use for the center and divide by the number of rows. If the result is a whole number then that center number will work.

For example:

Add: 1–11 = 66 – 6 (subtract the center number) = 60 ÷ 5 (divide by the number of rows) = 12 (the number the pairs have to equal)

The only other center number that will work is 1.

Solutions are:

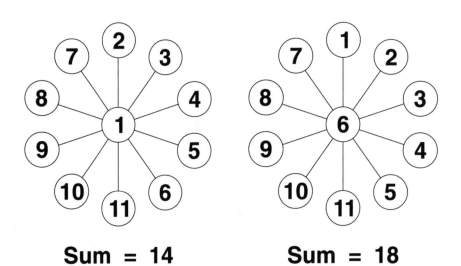

Sum = 14   Sum = 18

BIG MAGIC WHEEL

Use the numbers 1–11 so
that each of the five rows
has the same sum.

Notes on the Magic Octagon

This is a more difficult version of the Magic Wheel. It's easy enough to find the sum and the diameters if the techniques described on pages 34 and 36 are used. (It's more difficult to use trial and error now because there are so many numbers.)

Add 1–17 to get 153. Subtract the center number you are trying and divide by 8 (the number of diameters). If the result is a whole number, simply add the center number to it and you have the sum. If the result is not a whole number—try again.

The only numbers that will work in the center are 1 and 9.

$153 - 1 = 152 \div 8 = 19 + 1 = 20$

$153 - 9 = 144 \div 8 = 18 + 9 = 27$

Once you have determined the center number, the remaining numbers can be easily paired to make all the diameters equal the sum of 20 or 27.

However, this is only the first part of the problem. Now the diameter numbers must be manipulated to make the eight sides (of three numbers each) equal the same sum.

Using 1 in the center (for a sum of 20) you'll run into trouble almost immediately. In trying to make the side that includes the 17 equal 20 you'll see that you need the numbers 1 and 2. Of course the 1 is already being used in the center and the 2 is at the opposite end of the diameter.

The only sum that solves the whole problem is 27, with 9 in the center, as shown below.

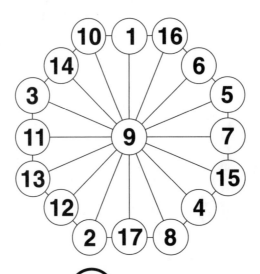

MAGIC OCTAGON

Use the numbers 1–17 so that each of the eight rows and each of the eight sides of the octagon has the same sum.

Notes on the Magic 3-Ring

Because this puzzle uses so few numbers most children will figure it out using experimentation and a bit of logic.

Children readily see that even if the four highest numbers are used in one ring the total would be no higher than 18. If the four lowest numbers are used, the sum would be no less than 10.

Clearly, using all the highest or lowest numbers on one ring makes it impossible to complete the other rings with an equal sum. Children can assume then that the solution sum will fall somewhere between 10 and 18.

Because each of the numbers in this puzzle is used exactly twice there is only one possible sum. It can be found using the following method:

Add the numbers 1–6 to get 21. Because each number is used twice, add 21 again. Divide the total by the number of rings (3) to get the magic sum of 14.

$21 + 21 = 42 \div 3 = 14$

A solution is:

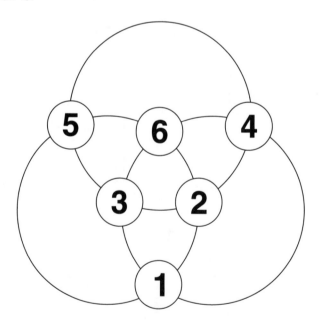

MAGIC 3-RING

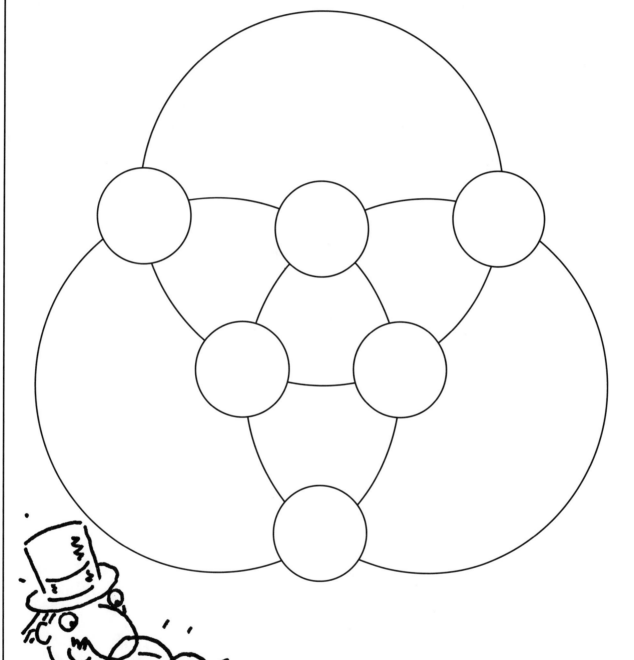

Use the numbers 1–6.

Each of the three rings must have the same sum.

Notes on the Magic 4-Ring

Because the Magic 4-Ring puzzle is quite a bit more complicated than the 3-Ring, experimentation and a little bit of logic probably won't be enough. Using the six lowest numbers in one ring would give us a sum of 21, the six highest numbers a sum of 57. As explained in the notes to the 3-Ring puzzle, these sums are not workable. Again, the actual sum must be somewhere in between. Given the number of possibilities, it is not likely that many children will be able to solve the problem by trial and error.

There is the chance that a particularly intuitive student might try 39, which is halfway between 21 and 57 (as 14 was halfway between 10 and 18 in the previous puzzle). In my experience this is unlikely, especially with younger children.

So unless your children have mastered the technique for finding the sum as outlined on page 40 (Magic 3-Ring) you may want to consider giving them the sum (39). This is what I do since my second graders don't know how to divide yet.

To find the sum, add 1 through 12 to get 78. Since each number is used in two rings, add 78 again. Then divide the total by the number of rings to get the magic sum.

$78 + 78 = 156 \div 4 = 39$

One solution is:

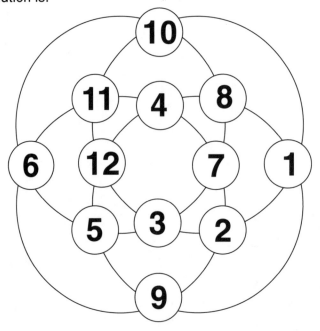

MAGIC 4-RING

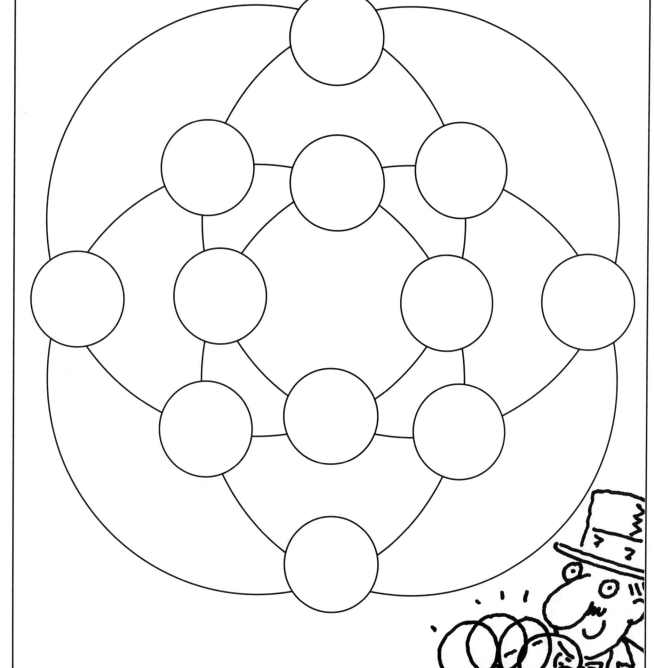

Use the numbers 1–12.

Each of the four rings must have the same sum.

Notes on the Magic Daisy

Starting with the previous puzzle, I generally begin to encourage my children to use calculators. Up until that point we've been working with addition facts and the earlier puzzles are a good way to practice them. But by now most of the children usually have the facts down pat.

The lowest possible sum for the magic daisy is 14—if 1, 2, 3, 4, and 5 are used in the middle. The highest sum is 19—if 6, 7, 8, 9, and 10 are used in the middle.

Solutions for these two sums are illustrated below. Challenge your class to discover whether other sums within the range of 14 and 19 are possible.

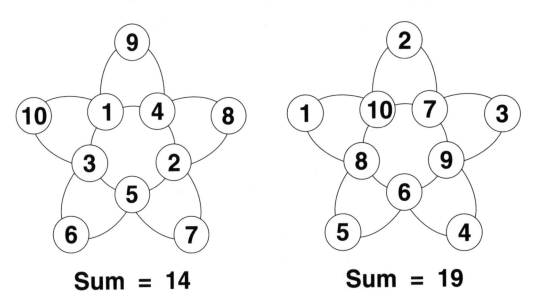

MAGIC DAISY

Use the numbers 1–10.

Each petal of the daisy must equal the same sum.

Notes on the Magic Links

My children are always delighted to use the calculator—but after the novelty has worn off some find they can add faster in their heads then they can manipulate the keys on the calculator.

A child once challenged me to an adding contest. He would add a series of numbers in his head while I added them on the calculator—he won.

Still, many children find calculators effective tools and become quite proficient in using them.

The Magic Links puzzle is essentially the same as the Magic Daisy with two extra links. The lowest possible sum is 19. The highest possible sum is 26. Once again, your students can try to find other sums that work within this range.

Solutions are:

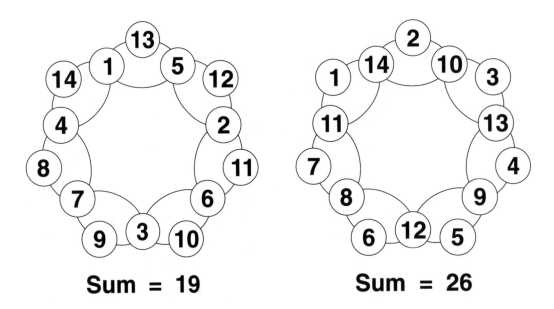

Sum = 19   **Sum = 26**

Name _____   Date _____

MAGIC LINKS

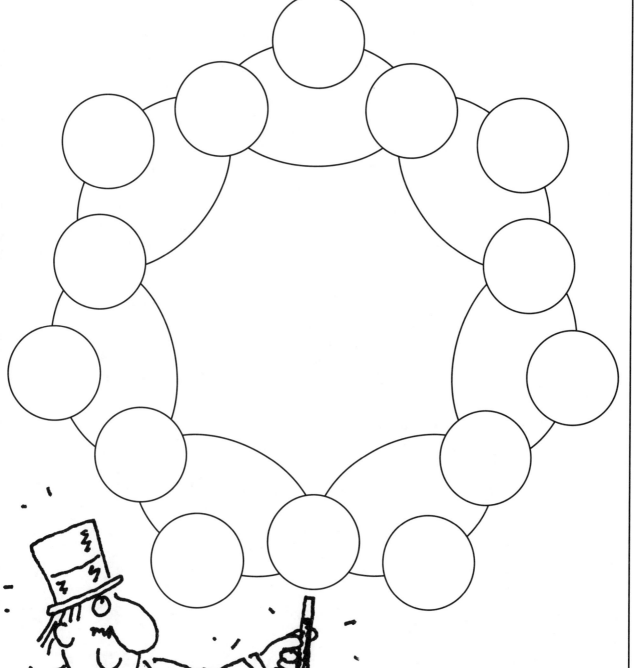

Use the numbers 1–14 so that each of the links has the same sum.

Notes on the Magic Rectangle

By now, most children are aware that many puzzles have more than one possible sum. This is the first in a series of puzzles that asks children to find solutions for several sums. Have children record their solutions in the small rectangles at the bottom of the puzzle page.

Even children who have no knowledge of the technique used to find the range of possible sums, in this case 17 (which has no solution) to 22, don't seem to have too much difficulty finding several solutions.

Most children by now have enough experience in solving number puzzles to make fairly accurate estimates of sums that will work. Once they come up with one solution they correctly assume that the other solutions will be slightly higher or slightly lower.

You will note that I generally ask children to find fewer sums than are actually possible (with the exception of the Little Magic Triangle). I've found through experience that having to determine more than three or four solutions for a particular problem becomes tedious for many children. You may, however, wish to issue a special challenge asking students to find all possible sums (perhaps without even telling them how many there are).

Possible solutions are:

1 9 8	1 10 8	10 8 2	10 4 8
4 5	4 6	5 3	2 3
7 3	5 2	1 6	1 5
6 10 2	9 7 3	4 7 9	9 7 6
Sum = 18	**Sum = 19**	**Sum = 20**	**Sum = 22**

MAGIC RECTANGLE

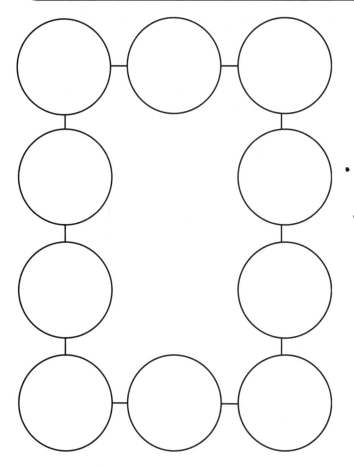

Use the numbers 1–10.

Each side of the rectangle must have the same sum. Find three different solution sums.

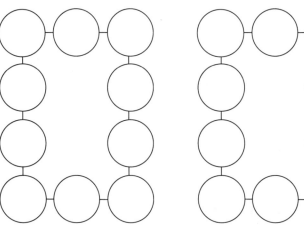
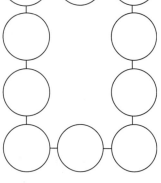
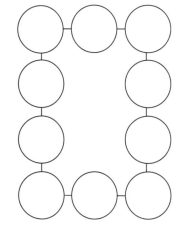

Sum = _____   Sum = _____   Sum = _____

Notes on the Magic X

This puzzle has five different solution sums. Challenge children to find four of them.

The following strategy can be used to solve the problem:

Add the numbers 1 through 9 to get a total of 45. To this add a vertex number (which will be used twice) and divide by 2 (the number of rows).

After trying a few numbers it becomes apparent that the vertex must be an odd number so that when it is added to 45 the total will be evenly divisible by 2.

All the numbers in the range (23 to 27) work as sums. Note that in all solutions except for 27 the numbers can be manipulated to make the total of the four outermost circles equal the sum, too.

Possible solutions are:

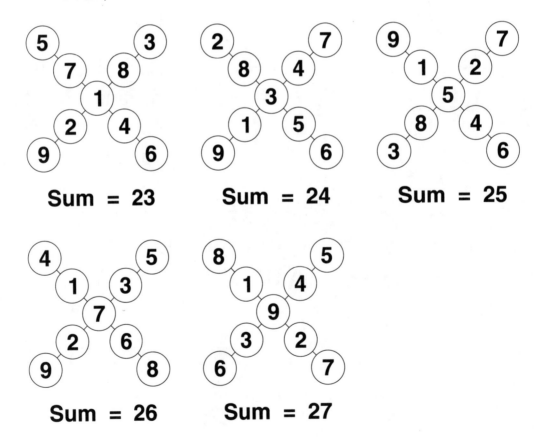

Sum = 23   Sum = 24   Sum = 25

Sum = 26   Sum = 27

MAGIC X

Sum = _____

Sum = _____

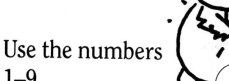

Use the numbers 1–9.

Each of the two rows must equal the same sum. Find four different solution sums.

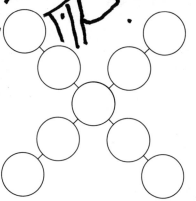

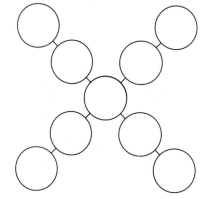

Sum = _____   Sum = _____

Notes on the Little Magic Triangle

The next three puzzles are all triangles of various sizes for which children are expected to find several solution sums.

The formula for finding the range of possible sums is the same for all:

$$\left(\begin{array}{c}\text{total of}\\\text{numbers}\end{array} + \begin{array}{c}\text{total of lowest}\\\text{possible}\\\text{intersection}\\\text{points}\end{array}\right) \div \begin{array}{c}\text{number}\\\text{of rows}\end{array} = \begin{array}{c}\text{lowest}\\\text{possible}\\\text{sum}\end{array}$$

$$\left(\begin{array}{c}\text{total of}\\\text{numbers}\end{array} + \begin{array}{c}\text{total of highest}\\\text{possible}\\\text{intersection}\\\text{points}\end{array}\right) \div \begin{array}{c}\text{number}\\\text{of rows}\end{array} = \begin{array}{c}\text{highest}\\\text{possible}\\\text{sum}\end{array}$$

My students have always been able to solve all three puzzles without using the formula.

Solutions for the Little Magic Triangle are:

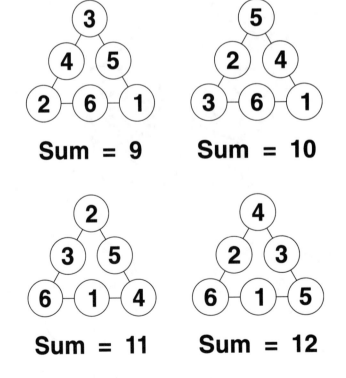

Sum = 9   Sum = 10

Sum = 11   Sum = 12

LITTLE MAGIC TRIANGLE

Use the numbers 1–6 so that each side of the triangle has the same sum. Find four different solution sums.

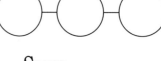

Sum = _____

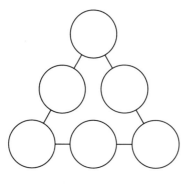

Sum = _____

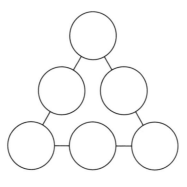

Sum = _____

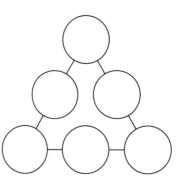

Sum = _____

Notes on the Big Magic Triangle

It's fun to watch how excited and encouraging the more advanced children become when their classmates are trying to figure out a puzzle that they themselves have already solved. They practically have to bite their tongues to keep from blurting out the answer.

"You're so close. You only have to switch two numbers." and (to me) "I'm not telling the answer. I'm only giving a hint." They are genuinely thrilled when another child succeeds.

The Big Magic Triangle has five solution sums (see p. 52 for the formula to determine the range of sums):

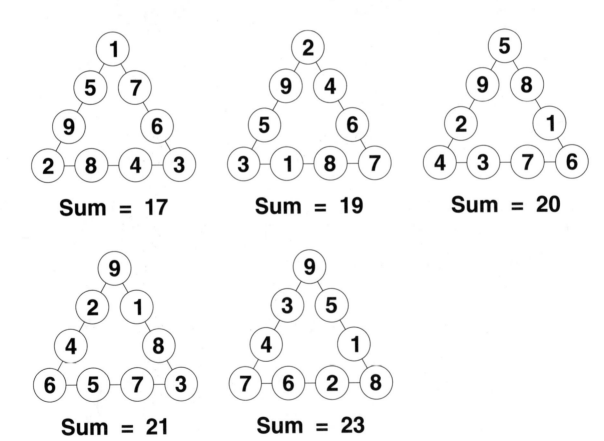

Sum = 17   Sum = 19   Sum = 20

Sum = 21   Sum = 23

BIG MAGIC TRIANGLE

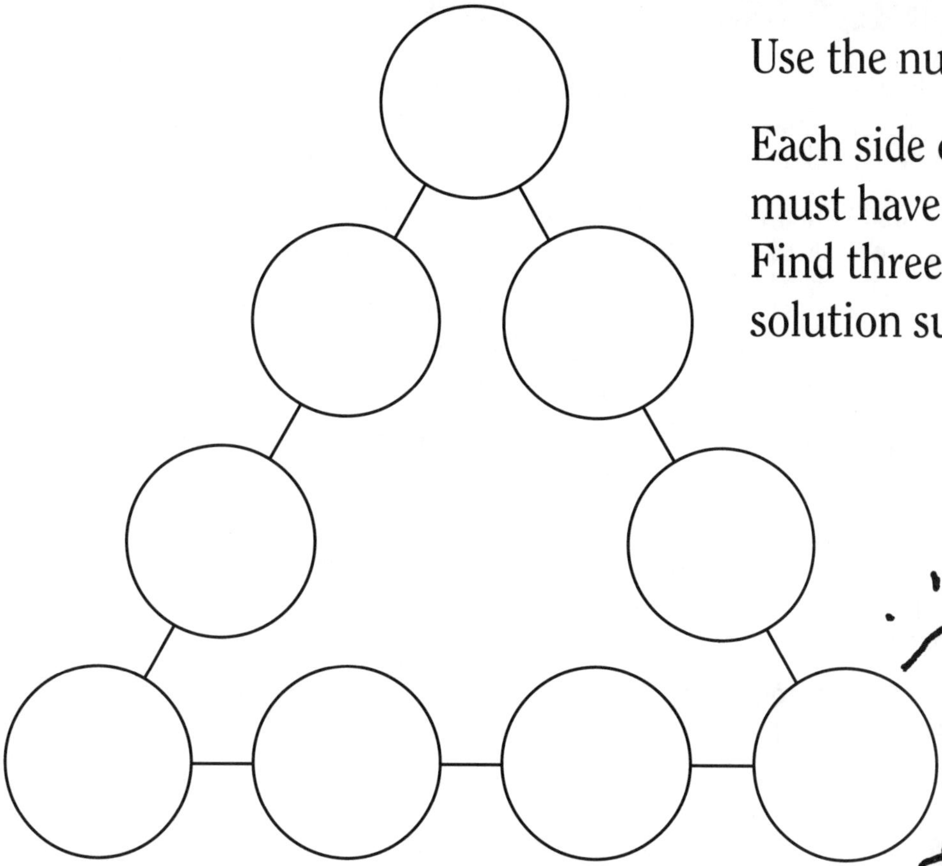

Use the numbers 1–9.

Each side of the triangle must have the same sum. Find three different solution sums.

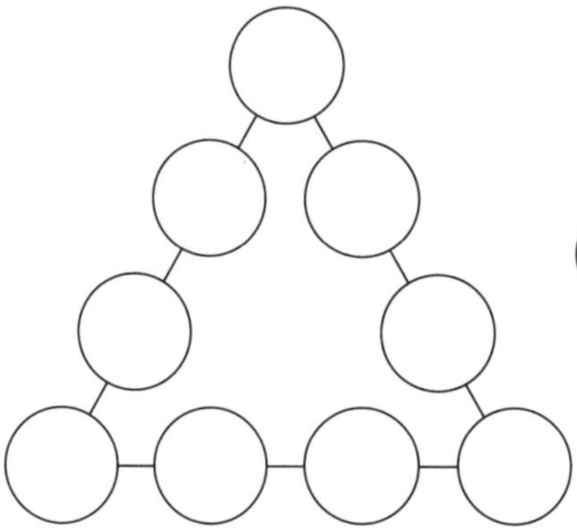

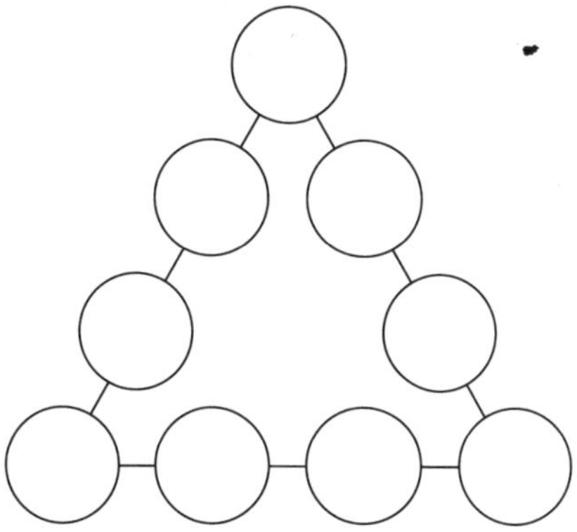

Sum = _____

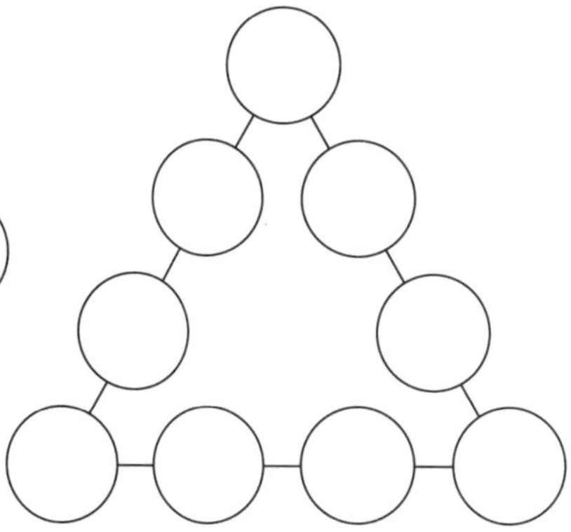

Sum = _____

Sum = _____

Notes on the Giant Magic Triangle

In the best of all possible worlds the children would solve a puzzle, record the answers, put the completed puzzle in the finished work box, and go on to the next puzzle. I would then check it when I had time.

It doesn't quite work out that way in my classroom. Most of the kids want their puzzles checked immediately—even before they write down the answers. This, of course, would necessitate my dropping whatever I'm doing to do a quick check. I must admit that I'm usually tempted to do just that. It's very hard to say, "Not now," or "You'll have to wait a little while," in the face of such excitement.

Luckily, help is at hand. The children who have already completed the puzzle in question rush right over to do the checking.

Everyone is happy. The more advanced children feel important and reinforce their own math skills when they are checking other children's work. The children whose puzzles are being checked receive the quick response they need.

The Giant Magic Triangle has ten solutions with sums 28 through 37 (see p. 52 for the formula to determine the range of sums):

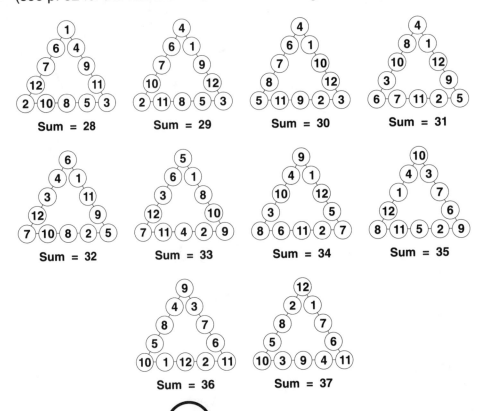

GIANT MAGIC TRIANGLE

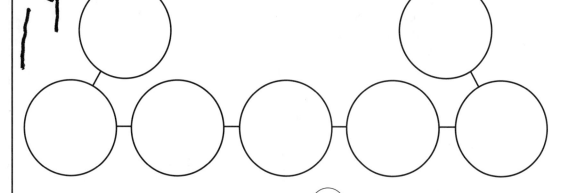

Use the numbers 1–12.

Each side of the triangle must have the same sum. Find three different solution sums.

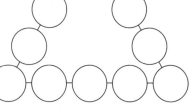

Sum = _____

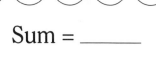

Sum = _____

Sum = _____

Notes on the Magic Snowflake

The Magic Snowflake is essentially a Magic Wheel with a twist. The techniques that worked to discover the center numbers and the sums for the Magic Wheels (pages 34 and 36) will work here. The twist is that the total of the six end numbers must equal that sum, too.

Using 10 as a center number, the remaining numbers can be placed as follows:

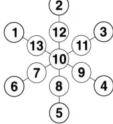

The highest numbers are placed nearest the center, clockwise, in descending order. The six lowest numbers are placed in the outer positions, clockwise, in ascending order. The sum of each row is now 37.

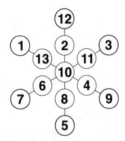

The numbers can now be easily manipulated within a row to make the six end numbers total 37.

The same pattern can be used with 1, 4, 7, or 13 in the center.

Other solutions are:

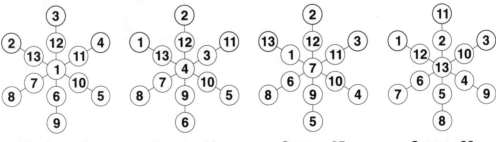

| Sum = 31 | Sum = 33 | Sum = 35 | Sum = 39 |

MAGIC SNOWFLAKE

Use the numbers 1–13 so that each of the three long rows has the same sum.

The total of the six end numbers must also equal that sum.

Notes on the Magic Tetrahedron

Because the remaining puzzles in this book are fairly complicated (due either to the numerous intersection points or the sheer volume of numbers), I always give my students the sums.

It took me several days to find a sum (31) that would work for the Tetrahedron even though I had calculated the range. Even finding the range (30 through 36) was more difficult than usual because some numbers are used three times and some twice.

Each of the four faces of the tetrahedron must equal 31. Younger children may have a problem visualizing this two-dimensional picture as a three-dimensional figure. I always show them a solid tetrahedron (from a set of wooden or plastic geometric solids) to help them "see" the faces.

Here is a solution for the sum 31. There may be other solution sums.

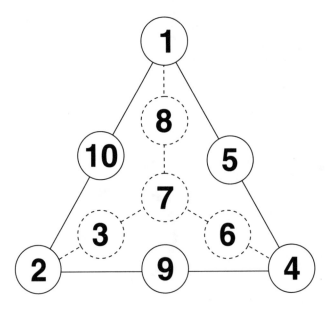

MAGIC TETRAHEDRON

Use the numbers 1–10. Each of the four faces of the tetrahedron must equal 31.

Notes on the Magic Pyramid

As the puzzles get more difficult they take longer to complete. More advanced students begin to get stuck and other children catch up. The number of children in each group gets larger and the number of groups gets smaller.

Everyone seems to be happy with this turn of events. The more advanced children are pleased to have more kids in their group because it gives them a better chance at solving the puzzle. The other children are delighted to have moved into a more advanced group.

In the Magic Pyramid the four triangular faces and the square base must equal 23. Again, the range is difficult to find since numbers may be used 2, 3, or 4 times. As with the Magic Tetrahedron you may want to use an actual square-based pyramid as a model.

A solution for the sum 23 is shown here. There may be other solution sums.

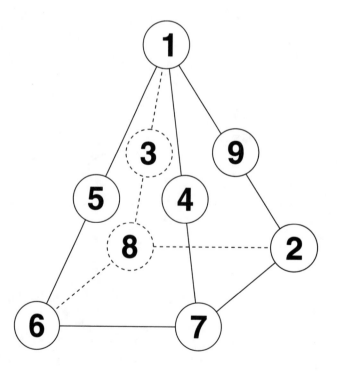

MAGIC PYRAMID

Use the numbers 1–9 so that each of the four triangular faces and the square base equals 23.

Notes on the
Magic 5-Point Star

Star puzzles have always been among the most difficult for my students. In this particular puzzle only ten of the numbers from 1 to 12 are used (7 and 11 are excluded).

The first time I presented the Magic 5-Point Star to a group, I did not tell them which of the twelve numbers would not be used. After watching the children experiment for several days it became apparent that because there was no logical way to figure out that the 7 and 11 should be eliminated—they would only stumble onto the information by chance (which might take all year). Thereafter I have always told students both the sum and the numbers to exclude.

For your information, the magic sum is determined in the following way: since each number in the puzzle is used exactly twice, find the sum by adding the numbers 1 through 12 (except 7 and 11) to get 60, multiplying by 2 and dividing by 5 (the number of rows). The only possible sum is 24. This technique works for all the star puzzles.

One arrangement is:

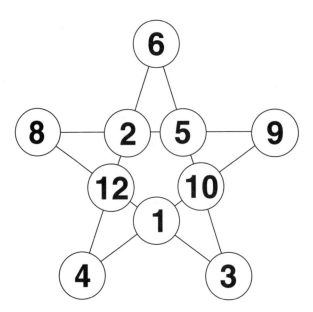

Name _____   Date _____

MAGIC 5-POINT STAR

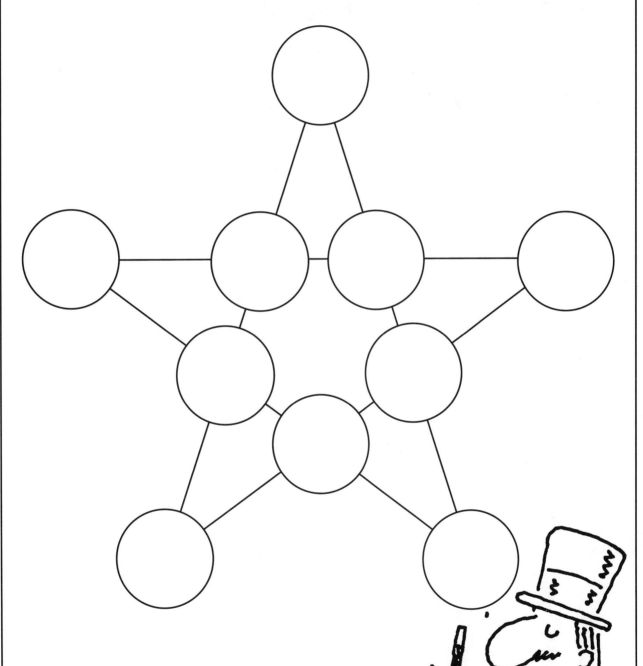

Use the numbers 1–12 except 7 and 11.

Each of the five rows must equal 24.

Notes on the
Magic 6-Point Star

The only problem that ever seems to come up with the groups is what to do when a child who has been working with a particular group is not there when the group solves the puzzle. Year after year children come up with their own ways of handling this problem.

1. If the child in question is absent, a group member simply takes that child's puzzle sheet and fills in the answer. (If the child is absent for an extended period and misses several puzzles, I generally intervene and either place the child with another group or send the puzzles home to be worked on.)

2. Frequently, one or two children from a group will work on a puzzle while the others are off doing something else (this happens quite often, especially when a puzzle takes several days— or weeks—to solve). It seems to be an acceptable practice and the whole group continues to share in the solution.

3. Sometimes a child will tire of these puzzles and completely drop out of the group. If a puzzle is solved after a child has left the group, the group usually declines to share the solution with him. Usually the excluded child sees the justice in this but occasionally there are hard feelings and I have to step in to arbitrate.

Here is a solution for the Magic 6-Point Star:

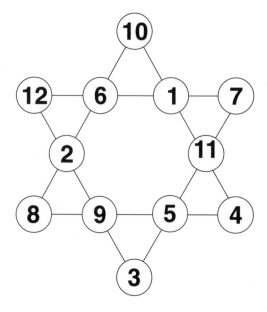

MAGIC 6-POINT STAR

Use the numbers 1–12.

Each of the six rows must equal 26.

Notes on the Magic 7-Point Star

I love to watch kids work on the star puzzles. All the boundaries that usually apply even when children work in groups seem to break down.

Two children may work on one puzzle paper. "I've got the answer!" becomes "We've got the answer!" My favorite, though, is when one child says, "I missed it by one row," and two other children immediately drop what they're doing to work on that row. I often overhear an exchange like this: One child says, "I'm so close but I just can't make it work." Another responds, "Here, you work on mine and I'll work on yours."

Here is a solution for the 7-Point Star:

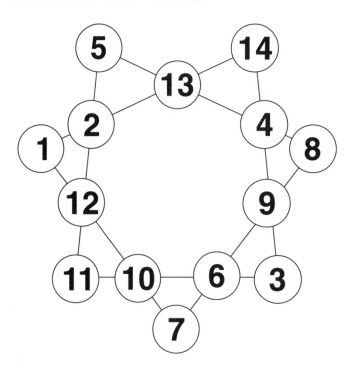

MAGIC 7-POINT STAR

Use the numbers 1–14.

Each of the seven rows must add up to 30.

Notes on the Magic 8-Point Star

For some reason this star seems to be much more difficult for kids then any of the other star puzzles. It often takes children several weeks to solve this puzzle. They work diligently, give up, then try again later.

This one is really fun to watch. A child, working all alone, announces to no one in particular, "I think I've got it!" The child is immediately surrounded by other members of the group who rush over from all points in the room.

There's great excitement as the group begins to check the rows until it's discovered that one row equals 35 instead of 34.

"Change the 7 and the 8!" suggests one child.

"Now that row is 35," says another.

"Try the 4 and the 6 and then change the 9 and 10," says the first, and so on. When nothing works it's back to the drawing board.

Here's one solution to the Magic 8-Point Star:

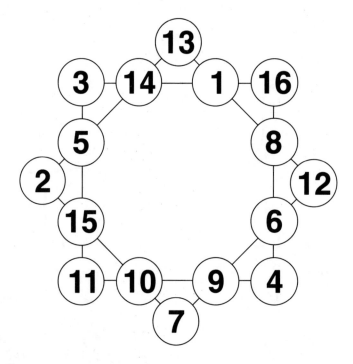

MAGIC 8-POINT STAR

Use the numbers 1–16 so that each of the eight rows equals 34.

Notes on the Big Magic Square

There is extensive literature written on the subject of magic squares. If a magic square has an even number of rows or columns it is called an even magic square. One with an odd number of rows or columns is an odd magic square.

There is no known method for solving every size of even magic squares but there is a method for this particular one—the 4 x 4 magic square.

Simply place the numbers 1–16 in order, as follows:

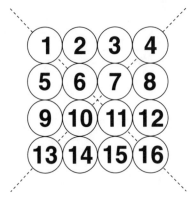

Exchange the numbers opposite each other along the diagonals.

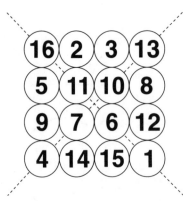

There are literally hundreds of other arrangements that will work to solve the puzzle.

Generally, this is the last puzzle that my students seriously work on and there have been several years when no one was able to solve it.

BIG MAGIC SQUARE

Use the numbers 1–16 so that
each row (horizontal, vertical,
and diagonal) equals 34.

Notes on the Giant Magic Square

Though a few children have attempted the 5 x 5 square, they are soon daunted by the magnitude of the undertaking. None of my kids has ever solved the Giant Magic Square.

There *is* a method for solving all odd-number magic squares. Directions for using this method, as well as the solution to the Giant Magic Square, follow:

1. Put the number 1 in the middle box, top row, and continue filling in the boxes (with 2, 3, 4, etc.) diagonally upward and to the right.

2. If a number lands in an imaginary box (as does the 2) put it in the same position in the real grid (in this case that means placing the 2 in the bottom row, 4th box) and continue moving diagonally upward to the right. Hint: If this process confuses your students, have them visualize superimposing the imaginary grid on the real grid to see where they should place the number. As they continue, students will find that the 3 lands in the real grid but the 4 falls in an imaginary box. Superimposing this imaginary grid on the real grid places the 4 in the third row, first box.

3. If the number is to be placed in a box that is filled (example: the box the 6 would go in is already occupied by the 1), place the number in the box just below the preceding number (i.e. the 6 goes beneath the 5) and continue diagonally upward.

	18	25	2	9	16	
17	24	1	8	15	17	
23	5	7	14	16	23	
4	6	13	20	22	4	
10	12	19	21	3	10	
11	18	25	2	9		

74

GIANT MAGIC SQUARE

Use the numbers 1–25 so that each row (horizontal, vertical, and diagonal) adds up to 65.

Notes on the Magic Honeycomb

I introduced this puzzle a couple of years ago as an alternate to the Giant Magic Square. Although several children have given it a try (intrigued, I think, by the shape), none were successful—nor did I expect them to be.

This puzzle appears in numerous books, always with the same solution. It seems to be the only one.

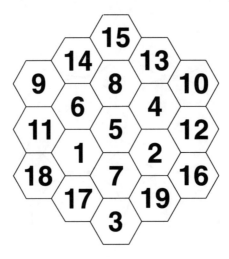

MAGIC HONEYCOMB

Use the numbers 1–19.

Each of the five vertical rows and each of the ten diagonal rows must add up to 38.

Number Disks

Cut out each disk. Store disks in an envelope or zip-lock bag to use again.

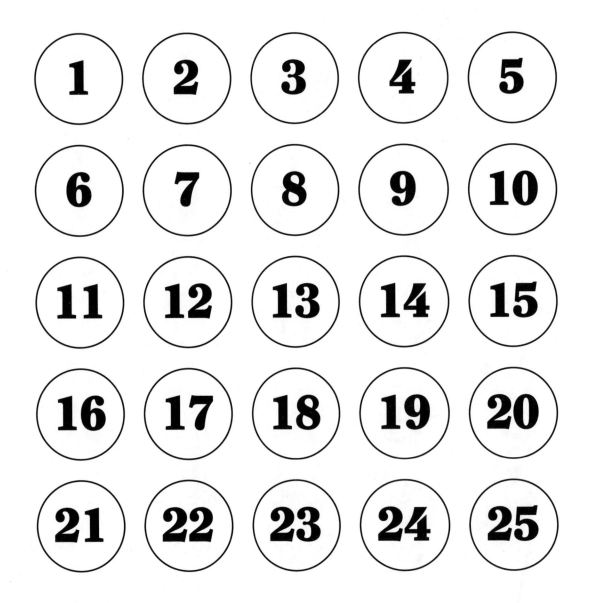

Final Notes

Visitors to my classroom are always amazed by the way children work on these puzzles. They watch the kids in action and marvel at the mathematical discussions that take place, the ease with which numbers are manipulated, and the cooperative efforts of the groups.

After many years it is still surprising, even to me, that on a Friday afternoon during "free time," (when students can do anything they want), three-quarters of my children choose to work on number puzzles.

An interesting event occurred this year. A former student, now in the fifth grade, came into my room and said, "I hear you have a new number puzzle. Can I have a copy?" In the days that followed several other fifth graders trooped in and out of my room to ask for the Magic Honeycomb. Evidently the interest remains, even years later.